KT-211-149

I.S.B.N. 0 85079 212 6

SUNDAY EXPRESS & DAILY EXPRESS
CARTOONS

Forty-fourth Series

AN EXPRESS BOOKS PUBLICATION

UK £2·95

FOREWORD

by

MAGNUS

MAGNUSSON, KBE

Writer

&

Broadcaster

It's the Giles family that gets me. They are so *family*. They are so gloriously, anarchically *his* that there could be no other family like them anywhere, and yet they somehow manage to be everybody's family.

Nobody's granny could be as awful as Grandma Giles, and yet there is something about her that is every indomitable granny who ever lived. The long-suffering mother, the self-absorbed teenagers, the hypochondriac Auntie Vera, the demonic children and their hapless pets – they are all hilariously over the top, yet with all the elements of family life so sharply sensed and so utterly recognisable that the heart warms while the stomach heaves into laughter.

Of course it's the little details lurking round the edges of the main subject of the cartoon that betray the special Giles hallmark: the baby unobtrusively strangling the cat, poor old Mum trying to do a mountain of ironing with one foot in the dog's dinner, Grandma tipping some gin into her bedtime cocoa. Giles crams the whole rich messy tapestry of life into one frame and makes us all laugh at ourselves, happy at knowing that we're not alone.

It's easy to forget, for those of us besotted with the Giles family, that Giles himself is at home anywhere in the world where human foibles and fashions could do with a bit of gentle mockery. Giles is as much at home at Ascot and Henley as he is among the lager louts at a football match or when he is taking an irreverent look at politicians and statesmen, despots and tycoons – and all the rest of us.

But why waste my breath? I cannot imagine anyone stopping to read this when they can plunge straight into these joyous pages to see what Giles has been getting up to this year. . . .

Magnus Magnusson

"Don't blame us—it's your damn Grandma making the landlady open every tin and food packet in the kitchen for inspection."

(Headline: Salmonella & listeria had been discovered in packed foods.)

"Keep your voice down, Grandma—the Colonel heard your remark: 'You don't mean to tell me the South Africans actually pay money for our cricketers'."

"At least it's doing me garden a bit of good."

"Beautiful, tranquil summer trip up the river—non-stop commentary of their first game of the season, blow by blow."

"Now they'll all be wanting one of their own—and I know who'll be head stable girl after a couple of weeks."

"And may there be no moaning at the bar when I put out to sea . . ." *Lord Tennyson*

"Mum can't find your tin hat, but she doesn't think you'll meet with a lot of flak between here and the pub."

"Richard says there's a lot more junk got to go. It doesn't come up to the same standard he had in his cell in Sweden."

"They moan all summer about the England cricketers, now they're moaning because the season's over."

"You're telling me that a nice man called and you sold him the car for this dear little Teddy bear because he told you they are making £55,000 each at Sotheby's?"

"There's always something sad about the last Sail of the Season."

"Kidnapping Mr Lawson won't cut the mortgages—he'll only be another mouth to feed. Take him back."

"We rescued him from the London Zoo."

"Thank the schools' new Lessons in Love—he wants to know who's been using his aftershave."

"She's bringing the game into disrepute again—blowing smoke over the pocket when I'm taking my shot."

"You're always saying get the old 'uns out and put us in. Well, here's your chance."

"The lady says there was a loud bang and her hat flew over the top of the church—mind if I have a look at those binoculars?"

"If there are any women vicars around they want to keep an eye on Corporal Rambo here—I had trouble with him in 1944."

"Stop laughing! Don't you want Daddy to look nice on his first TV show in Parliament on Tuesday?"

"She's not in a very good mood—we've been knocking on 10 Downing Street all afternoon and the Policeman told her the job's for MPs only."

"I bet he didn't buy those sugar meece because he likes them—he bought them because you don't get nicked for buying them on a Sunday."

"The new rule—we all bow out of the room walking backwards since he's been made a King in the Christmas play."

GILES wishes all his readers a Merry Christmas. He is not feeling very Christmassy himself as he has been in hospital to have a ~~kitty cat~~ cataract taken out of his eye.

The Surgeon says he hopes to have him back to the old drawing board by next Sunday.

giles jr.

While Giles was hors de combat for an eye operation, this announcement appeared in the *Sunday Express*

"Oh dear, they all left an hour ago—they thought they were staying with *you* for Christmas."

"I suppose you realise the Germans the French and the Japs went back to work last Wednesday?"

"If we sneaked all our customer's private desires and passions to the Press what do you think they'd make?"

"You don't call an ambulance every time you find one of them sitting down."

"If that's a reply from the Post Office to my letter giving them a rollicking you're three days late!"

" 🎵 We're singing in the rain 🎵 ."

"Before you rush off to cricket you might clean Butch up for Crufts."

"Morning luv—still writing your letter to Gatting?"

(Headline: England cricketers who toured South Africa were getting a bad press.)

"Hazel, I'm damned if I'm going to salute you every time you fetch my drink!"

"I thought you were going to tackle Grandma about paying her own poll tax."

"Now they look like lifting sanctions on South Africa you needn't have planted those three hundred orange trees."

"I explained that your stately home is not open until Easter, but she says she wants to have a chat about her Poll Tax and yours."

"Dad handed in his war medals in protest against the Poll Tax but the Corporal told him to take them home and clean 'em up."

"You know the book you ran on the Gold Cup? There's a queue at the door saying they all backed the 100–1 winner."

"Dad—Mum sent me over these for you to bring her for Mother's Day."

"Yet another Eugenie, I'm afraid, Oh Lord."

"You in there—I hear you and Mr Fisk had a good National after you dropped me off at the first fence."

"If you can't tell the difference between a Doomsday Gun and a 2" galvanised pipe you're a long way off making Chief Constable."

(Headline: Police discover supergun being smuggled to Iraq.)

"The lady says she paid 50p into the fund and she's entitled to have a drive."

Veteran finds a safe port

FALKLANDS War veteran HMS Plymouth, rescued by *Sunday Express* readers from Royal Navy target practice, will be handed over to the Warship Preservation Trust in Plymouth on Friday.

The frigate was bought from the Defence Ministry after our appeal fund passed its £200,000 target. It will be preserved as a "floating history lesson" and national memorial to all who served in the South Atlantic.

The VIP reception, hosted by *Sunday Express* editor Robin Morgan, will take place on board the frigate, anchored in the River Tamar, at midday.

Vice-Admiral Sir Alan Grose, the Flag Officer, Plymouth will hand over the vessel to Sir Donald Gosling, chairman of the appeal, who personally donated £100,000. Sir Donald will then formally pass on ownership to Sir Philip Goodhart, Tory MP for Beckenham and chairman of the Trust.

Among the guests will be former commanding officers of the Plymouth and crew members who won decorations for bravery in the Falklands. For many of them it will be their first reunion since the war.

The day will be marked with Royal Navy fly-pasts, stunts by Express Newspapers' Pitts Special biplane and the Flying Crusader girls parachuting in.

The appeal fund is still open and further donations will go towards maintenance of the frigate, which will have a permanent home at Gosport near HMS Victory.

"We'll change the station—Auntie Vi wants us to see her Christmas family videos."

"Dad, does Prince Philip's list include the gentlemen at the table behind you?"

"I assure you signora—we are not Inglese football louts over here for the World Cup."

"Your MP says you admonished him for wearing sneakers."

(Headline: The Speaker of the House of Commons warned scruffy MP's to smarten up.)

"Threatening football referees is one thing—slapping Flower Show judges because you didn't get a Highly Commended is another!"

"I'm not having an extra litter a year to please him. Or you."

(Headline: Because of the mad cow scare the public were not buying beef.)

"Dad, why does the vicar preach to us that smoking and cars are destroying the world—then ends up with 'world without end, Amen'?"

"If you can leave your conference on Bobby Robson we might perhaps commence dictation."

"I can't wait to see my old man's face when I tell him he's got a couple of Chelsea buns for dinner instead of roast beef."

EPSOM

EPSOM

EPSOM

"That diabolical monstrosity, as you call it—you must make allowances for him painting with his left hand."

"This gondolier's giving 100–1 Archbishop Runcie doesn't take over from Bobby Robson."

"Young man, we're not pinching your wind—if we wanted your wind we'd ask for it."

"I think they're plotting to take you out to tea for Father's Day."

ASCOT

ASCOT

ASCOT

"What's the betting she opens with 'The longest day's gone, the nights are drawing in—soon be Christmas'?"

"Thanks to your clever young brother singing 'ere we go, 'ere we go at Henley . . ."

"You've no right to ask Vicar if he's running a book on the new Archbishop of Canterbury."

"Butch, according to the vote everybody except the cat thinks it's worth £20 a year to keep you on the road."

(Headline: Dog owners were threatened with £20 registration fee.)

"I only said if the Germans take over, Grandma would make a first-class head Gauleiter."

"She might have the makings of a great soprano, but this Madonna-minder treatment is absurd."

"What'll it be, Sir—a clipped toothbrush moustache with a forelock flowing over the forehead, or the new Princess Diana short back and sides?"

"She wrapped up in rugs just like the Mexicans do to keep cool. Now she wants a hot water bottle because she's too cold."

"I expect you will be getting your papers to rejoin the Bengal Lancers any day now, Colonel."

"To the best of my knowledge there are no Iraqi snipers on our route today, Madam."

"What an escape from the Gulf crisis—watching Chalkie on holiday!"

"Went head over heels giving One an extra special curtsy"

(Headline: Prince Charles had another operation on his broken arm.)

"I read in the paper the police had been told to stop being rude to the public."

"Here comes your missus—I think she wants a chat about you thinking of turning the farm into a golf course."

"I get a little tired of them asking me to explain the Middle East situation to them."

"What an extraordinary thing to tell us to do with our empty tea cups."

"Hold tight Gascoigne, she's had enough of Gazzamania."

"If the French don't want our lamb why don't we tell them we won't let them have any?"

"This'll please him, the Gulf bill is costing a million pounds a day and petrol's gone up to £2.30 a gallon."

"Maybe he can't spell four letter words, but he knows how to use them."

(Headline: Tests prove one in six children can't spell four letter words.)

"If Mrs. Thatcher is staying on until she's 70, Grandma will be over 200."

"If I were you, Vera, I'd get Mr. Bush and Saddam Hussein to split the bill."

"Dad, why is Grandma rewriting Land Of Hope and Glory? She always belts it out louder than anyone else."

"I don't know about Prince William having detectives to guard him—it's the detectives that would want guarding around here."

"Dad! Gary Lineker is the new England captain!"

"None of 'em will ever learn – I got six across the backside for writing 'Peace' on the school wall when I were a boy."

"Dad — if Mum's going to wear her old uniform for the Battle of Britain Service, can I sit right at the other end of the pew?"

"Two extra pints, please,"

The following are from a series of
Christmas Cards designed for
The Royal National Lifeboat Institution
and the Game Conservancy Trust.

"I'm not Santa Claus!
We were having our Christmas
party when your 'May Day'
came in."

Cartoons reproduced under licence from Express Newspapers plc.

CARTOON GIFTS

TABLE MATS:

SERIES I
(Giles' personal selection)

SERIES II
(General Humour)

GOLF SERIES
(Golfing cartoons)

CARTOON GIFTS